LEARN
TOGETHER
ENGLISH

ENGLISH TESTS 200

200 punctuation questions

Richard Dawson

Macmillan
Children's Books

First published 1996 by Macmillan Children's Books
a division of Macmillan Publishers Limited
25 Eccleston Place, London SW1W 9NF
and Basingstoke

Associated companies throughout the world

ISBN 0 330 34551 6

Copyright © Macmillan Children's Books 1996.
Text and illustrations by Richard Dawson.

9 8 7 6 5 4 3 2 1

A CIP catalogue record for this book is available from the British Library.

Typeset by Macmillan Children's Books. Printed by Henry Ling Ltd, The Dorset Press, Dorchester.

Fill in the capital letters, full stops, commas and question marks for these sentences.

i like school

_____

my house is in the town

_____

where do you play

_____

i like to play in the park

_____

sweets are nice to eat

_____

have you been to london

_____

mary had her holiday in brighton

_____

the dog chased the cat

_____

the duck ate the bread

_____

rajesh bought a football

_____

jenny supports manchester united

_____

the eagle flew high in the sky

_____

it is always hot in jamaica

_____

does it rain in spain

_____

do you like doughnuts

_____

has your cat got better

_____

my dad ate all the jelly

_____

would you like to come to my party

_____

do you like egg sandwiches

_____

how many chickens laid eggs

_____

how do you start the motorbike

_____

the rain came in through the roof

_____

the sea in the caribbean is bright blue and as
clear as crystal

_____

_____

the dog wagged its tail when it got a sausage

_____

how many are coming to the party

_____

eric did not like the food he had on his french
holiday

_____

_____

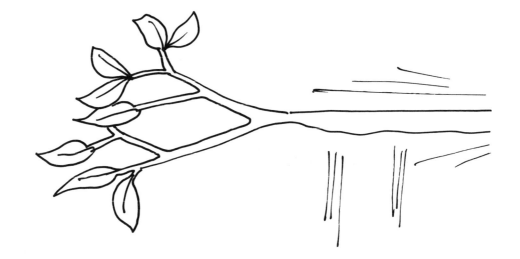

can an ostrich fly

_____

do fish sleep

_____

what makes a bee buzz

_____

elizabeth is the queen of england

_____

do you have sugar in your tea

_____

the african elephant has bigger ears than the indian elephant

_____

_____

does a swallow fly all the way to south africa

_____

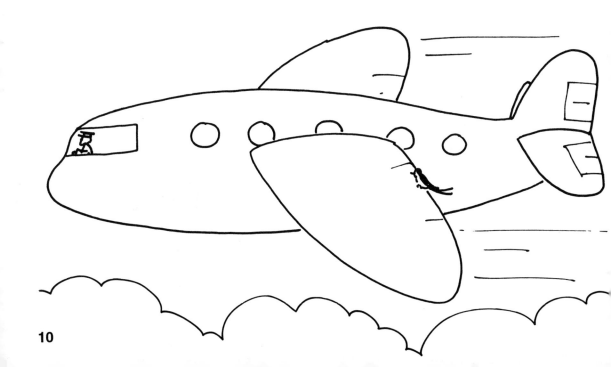

Note to parents

Each day when your children come home from school you wonder what they have learned at school. What do children do in English? When do they learn to punctuate? **Tests 200** shows the kind of punctuation they should be able to use at the end of their third year in school. Some of the sentences may be hard for your child. Help them by reading the text out loud and pausing where commas and full stops should go. Enjoy this book with your child, and if your child experiences difficulty with punctuation do not worry but have a quiet word with their teacher.

This pull-out centre section gives the answers and guidance on letter formation for you to practise with your child.

It is important that letters are formed correctly. Here is a guide . . . .

a b c d e f g
h i j k l m n
o p q r s t u
v w x y z

Practise on these.

a b c d e f g
h i j k l m n
o p q r s t u
v w x y z

ANSWERS

p3
I like school.
My house is in the town.
Where do you play?
I like to play in the park.
Sweets are nice to eat.

p4
Have you been to London?
Mary had her holiday in Brighton.
The dog chased the cat.
The duck ate the bread.

p5
Rajesh bought a football.
Jenny supports Manchester United.
The eagle flew high in the sky.
It is always hot in Jamaica.

p6
Does it rain in Spain?
Do you like doughnuts?
Has your cat got better?

p7
My dad ate all the jelly.
Would you like to come to my party?
Do you like egg sandwiches?
How many chickens laid eggs?
How do you start the motorbike?

p8
The rain came in through the roof.
The sea in the Caribbean is bright blue and as clear as crystal.
The dog wagged its tail when it got a sausage.
How many are coming to the party?
Eric did not like the food he had on his French holiday.

p9
Can an ostrich fly?
Do fish sleep?
What makes a bee buzz?

p10
Elizabeth is the Queen of England.
Do you have sugar in your tea?
The African elephant has bigger ears than the Indian elephant.
Does a swallow fly all the way to South Africa?

p15

Nigel scored a goal for United in the last minute.

Kathryn has a pony called Penny, William has a pony called Fudge.

Rory Underwood plays rugby for England and Leicester.

p16

I would like to know how they get the jam in the middle of a doughnut.

The English beat the French at the Battle of Waterloo.

The RSPCA looks after animals that have not been treated well.

p17

At Christmas time Santa Claus brings lots of good things.

Louise was reading 'Swiss Family Robinson' on the train journey to Leeds.

Many people do not like smoking.

p18

There are many different countries in South America including Chile and Peru.

Paddington Bear travelled all the way from Peru to Paddington Station
in London.

The Evening Telegraph reported the Christmas fair in St. James' Church.

p19

The pilot from the RAF flew a Spitfire at the North London air show.

How did the policeman know that the crime was committed in Scotland?

Would you like a slice of apple pie?

p20

Do you want a ticket for Wednesday or Thursday?

The fisherman returned in his boat 'The Seagull' with his catch of crabs
and lobsters.

p21

William the Conqueror invaded England in 1066 and during the battle King Harold was
killed.

Does your brother James like his new job in New Zealand?

The teacher told Alan to stay in at playtime.

p22

The smallest bird in England is the Jenny Wren.

The dogs, Kitt and Bonnie, ran all the way down the road to the butcher's.

Have you enjoyed this book?

nigel scored a goal for united in the last minute

---

kathryn has a pony called penny, william has a pony called fudge

---

---

rory underwood plays rugby for england and leicester

i would like to know how they get the jam in the middle of a doughnut

_____

_____

the english beat the french at the battle of waterloo

_____

_____

the rspca looks after animals that have not been treated well

_____

_____

at christmas time santa claus brings lots of
good things

_____

_____

louise was reading 'swiss family robinson' on
the train journey to leeds

_____

_____

many people do not like smoking

_____

there are many different countries in south america including chile and peru

_____

_____

paddington bear travelled all the way from peru to paddington station in london

_____

_____

the evening telegraph reported the christmas fair in st. james' church

_____

the pilot from the raf flew a spitfire at the north london air show

_____

_____

how did the policeman know that the crime was committed in scotland

_____

_____

would you like a slice of apple pie

_____

do you want a ticket for wednesday or thursday

_____

_____

the fisherman returned in his boat 'the seagull' with his catch of crabs and lobsters

_____

_____

william the conqueror invaded england in 1066 and during the battle king harold was killed

_____

_____

does your brother james like his new job in new zealand

_____

_____

the teacher told alan to stay in at playtime

_____

the smallest bird in england is the jenny wren

_____

the dogs, kitt and bonnie, ran all the way down
the road to the butcher's

_____

_____

have you enjoyed this book

_____

Are you at the top of the tree?
Fill in your score.

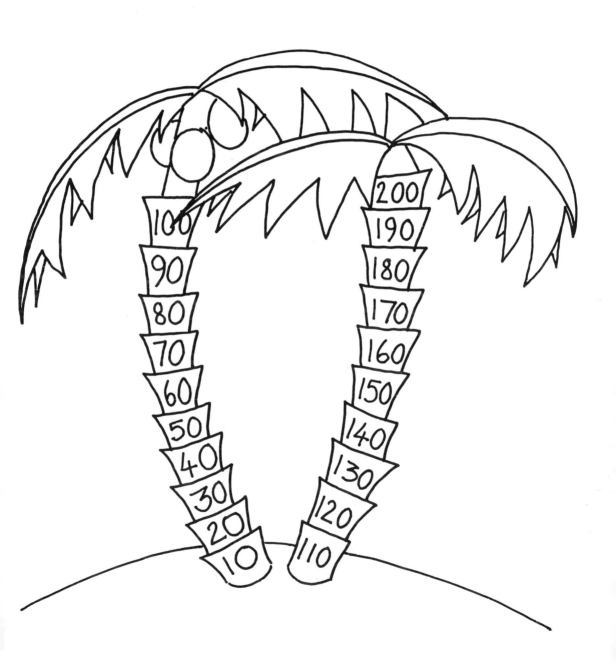

Can you find the commas, full stop and question mark Monkey has hidden?